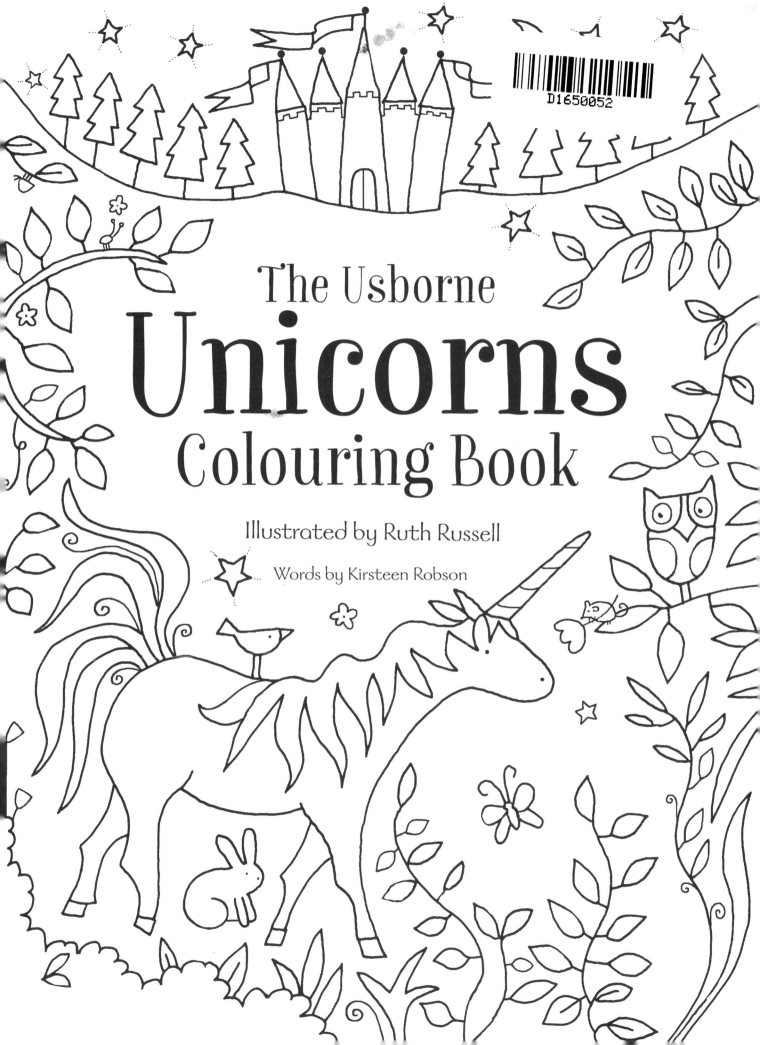

The Usborne
Unicorns
Colouring Book

Illustrated by Ruth Russell

Words by Kirsteen Robson

In a forest's leafy glade,
unicorns rest on the
cool, green grass.

3

These unicorns are watching the sparkling stream slipping under the bridge.

Unicorns love the sweet smell of ripe orchard fruits.

Silver-winged unicorns
swoop and soar between
the clouds and rainbows.

These unicorns have
climbed high into the
mountains to see
the sun rise.

Unicorns live in
the land of dreams
and fairy tales.

13

These unicorns are looking at the sea creatures in the clear, shallow water.

15

A gallop across snow-cloaked fields will help keep this unicorn warm.

16

18

The unicorns enjoy watching the wildlife as they bathe in the shady pool.

19

Little birds fill the air with the songs of spring.

Hush, little mice!
Don't disturb this
sleeping unicorn!

This royal unicorn stands alone in
the pale light of the moon.

This edition first published in 2019 by Usborne Publishing Ltd., Usborne House, 83-85 Saffron Hill, London EC1N 8RT, England.
www.usborne.com Copyright © 2019, 2018 Usborne Publishing Ltd. The name Usborne and the devices ♀⊕ are Trade
Marks of Usborne Publishing Ltd. All rights reserved. No part of this publication may be reproduced, stored in
a retrieval rsystem or transmitted in any form or by any means, electronic, mechanical, photocopying,
recording or otherwise without the prior permission of the publisher. UE. Printed in China.